Trace the straight lines of the spider's web.

Trace over the missing letters to complete the words.

Bugs Bugs

Well done! ✓

BbBb   CcCc

Trace over the light trails left by the fireflies.

Draw lines to match up the two halves of the creepy crawlies.

 Hmmm hmmm!

Dd Dd   Ee Ee

Help the bees find their way to the hive.

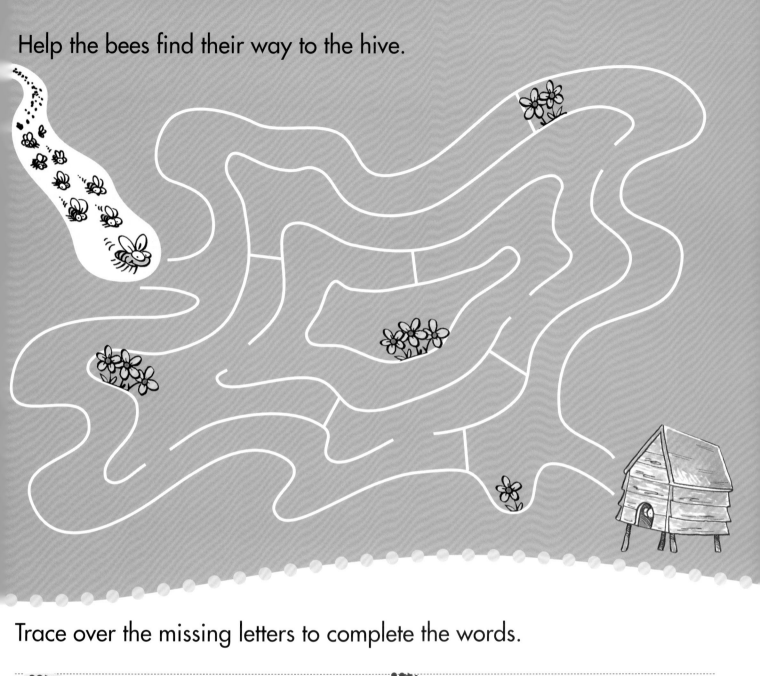

Trace over the missing letters to complete the words.

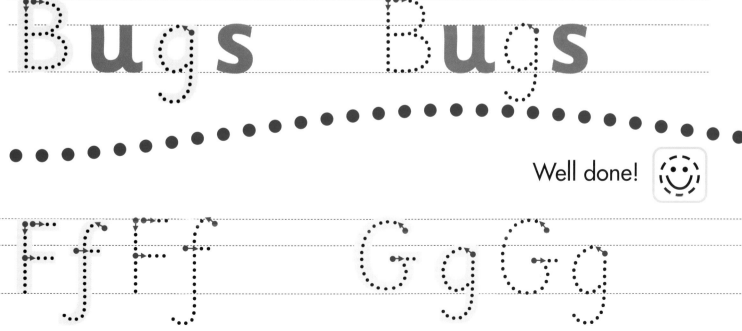

Bugs   Bugs

Well done!

Ff Ff   Gg Gg

Trace over the lines on the millipede's body.

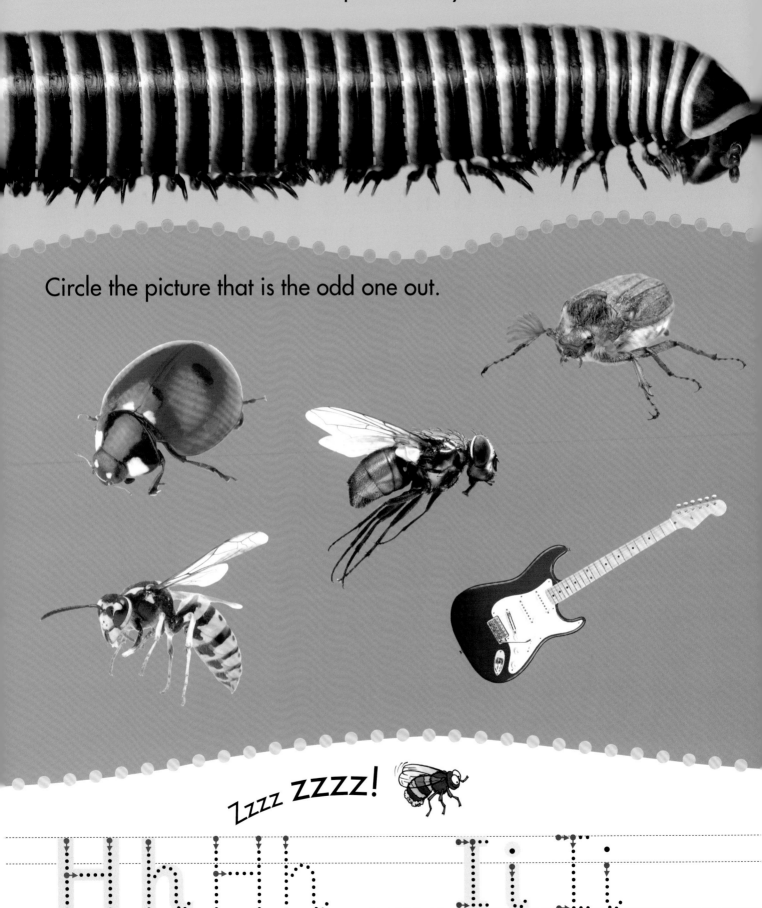

Circle the picture that is the odd one out.

Zzzz zzzz!

Hh Hh   Ii Ii

Find three differences between the two pictures and circle them.

Well done!

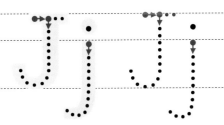

Trace over the line where the grasshopper has jumped.

Boing!

Circle what colour the butterfly is.

Green

Red

Blue

Yellow

Buzz buzz!

Ll Ll Ll Mm Mm

Draw around the ladybird's spots.

Follow the line to help the ants get to the sticky cake.

Yum
yum!

Well done!

NnNn OoOo

Draw in the bodies and legs
of the fighting stag beetles.

How many bees are on
the honeycomb? Write
the number in the box.

P p P p   Q q Q q

Trace the curvy line to show the snail's slimy trail.

Draw in the dragonfly's tail.

Trace over the missing letters to complete the words.

Bugs   Bugs

Hmmm hmmm!

Well done!

Rr Rr   Ss Ss

Trace over the line where the ladybird has flown.

Draw the spider's legs.

Trace over the missing letters to complete the words.

Bugs   Bugs

TtTt   UuUu

Draw the Atlas moth.

Circle the noises a bee makes.

Beep beep!

Hmmm hmmm!

Woof woof!

Buzz buzz!

Zzzz zzzz!

Zzzz zzzz!

Well done!

V v v v v   W w w w w

Draw over the lines to get to the bugs.

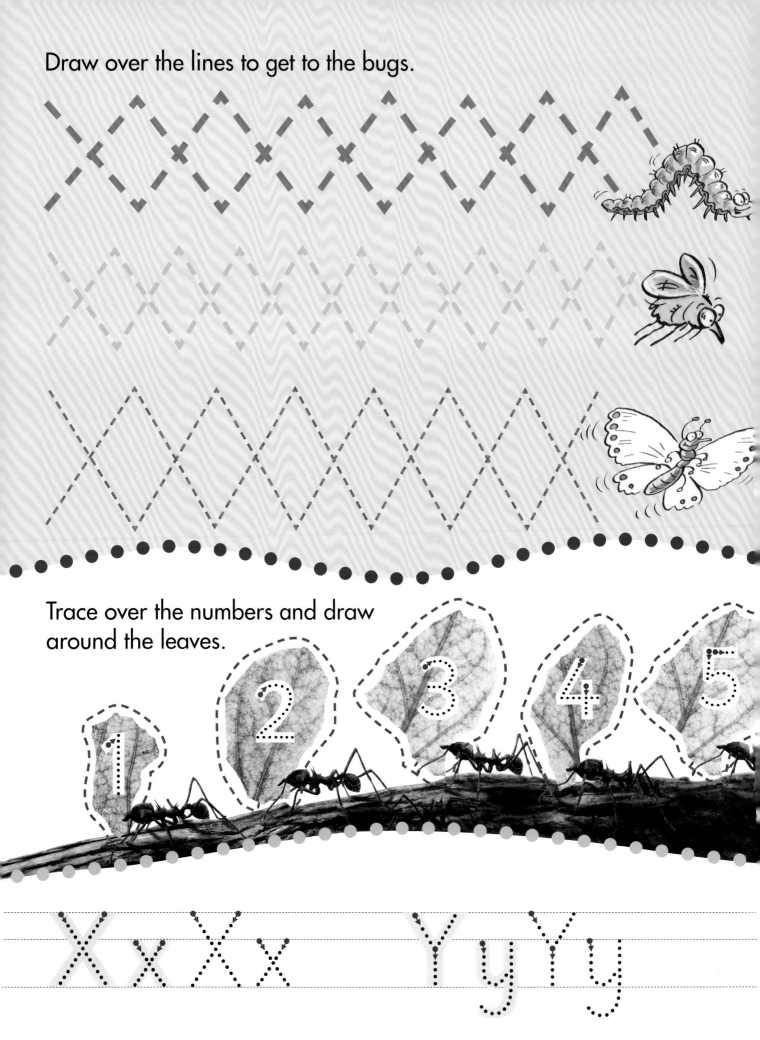

Trace over the numbers and draw
around the leaves.

1 2 3 4 5

X x X x   Y y Y y